ENDORSEMENTS

Chad Johnson
Title: Chief Inspiration Officer
Organization: The Giant 5 Guy

"This book is such a simple story with a mighty message. It is critical our children know they are wonderfully created by God and designed with a purpose to fulfill. Helping a child understand this is such a blessing and sets them up to be bulletproof from the insults of others. Every parent should read this book to their child."

Travis Adams
Title: Co-Founder & President
Organization: GravyStack

"This book is a true gem! Steven has spun a delightful tale that will enchant both children and parents alike. The vivid illustrations cohesively complement the lovable and relatable characters, making this book an absolute joy to read. But it's not just a delightful story - the message it imparts is both heartwarming and crucial. What better gift can we pass on than to see our children living out their true identity? This book will leave a lasting impression on your heart and soul."

Connor Gallagher

Title: CEO

Organization: TAN Books/Good Will Publishers

"As a father of fifteen, I know the daily battle to preserve our children in truth and joy. It is the simple things that light up the soul! In Steven Neuner's latest achievement, Are You A Tree? brings peace to the little ones among us, peace that can only be found in truth. In a world of confusion, here we have simplicity; in a world of frustration, here we have a spark of joy. From one father to another, thank you, Steven!"

Lee Bower

Title: Founder

Organization: Empowered Wealth

"I enjoyed reading "Are You A Tree?" by Steven J. Neuner, a children's book with a message that applies to everyone. This short simple story teaches an important lesson about self-acceptance and self-worth. It delivers a powerful message that helps children of all ages understand their value and that they are loved just as they are. It is a great reminder to me that even I am a child of God."

Holly Snell
Title: Chief Executive Officer
Organization: HOPE Women's Center

"This book is a MUST READ for every child who may be struggling with labels and words that bring harm and discouragement. Not only that, it is a reminder to every reader and hearer that OUR WORDS MATTER! Scripture reminds us that our words can produce LIFE or death – HOPE or despair. Steven's creativity has communicated this point in a clever and compelling way. This simple, yet profound book put a smile on my face and uplifted my heart with every page turned."

Sam Kelly
Title: Youth Pastor
Organization: Fellowship Church

"As a Youth Pastor I see firsthand the power that words have over young people and how they can impact their identity for the better or worse. It is why I believe it is imperative that books like "Are You A Tree?" are written. Steven both lightheartedly and yet poignantly stirs the hearts of young children with his writing to remind them of their intrinsic value in Christ. A message that is desperately needed today!"

Mary Miller
Title: Chairperson of the Board
Organization: JANCOA Janitorial Services

"As a grandmother, I am always on the lookout for books that my grandchildren will enjoy and learn from. "Are You A Tree?" is one of those books. Steven has written a captivating story that is both entertaining and engaging. The message is profound and timely for both children and any adult who has ever struggled with low confidence."

Brandon Lee
Title: Founder & President
Organization: BMX Local

"This book cuts through the seemingly strong forces of peer influence. Steven offers a lighthearted and Fatherly approach to a tough topic within our kids experience. The silly characters and playful illustrations compliment the message to engage the reader, both children and adults. Well done!"

Are You A Tree?

Steven J. Neuner

ethos
collective

DEDICATION

"Sticks and stones may break my bones,
but words will never hurt me."
1862 Anti-Bullying Quote

This book is dedicated to anyone who has experienced this quote to be untrue.

To anyone ever wounded by something that someone said or possibly worse, something never said that was needed.

To anyone who sometimes says things about and to themselves that they would NEVER think to say about another.

To anyone who feels called to lead and struggles with the courage to expose themselves in a mixed-up world where everyone has an opinion and a platform to share it.

This book is for anyone like me.

Are You A Tree?

Steven J. Neuner

ethos
collective

INTRODUCTION

All kids get called names at some point, but the real challenge is not letting those silly labels stick to us!

This adventure began when I was just four years old, and our family visited Chick-Fil-A. As a kid, I was thrilled about their super fun playground! One day, I joined the other kids in a lively game of tag. But suddenly, they all started calling me "monster" and ran away as if their lives depended on it! My feelings were hurt, and I ran to my parents with tears in my eyes.

After I told them what happened, my dad asked me if I was a monster. I shook my head no. He then told me that I was a tree! I insisted I wasn't a tree either. He playfully argued that if HE said I was a tree, then it MUST be true! I firmly repeated that I was NOT a tree.

From that day on, my dad used this same analogy whenever I felt down about being called names or wrestling with fitting in with peer groups or stereotypes. It was our special reminder that later became one for my younger sister and brother too!

In "Are You A Tree?," children will discover that the world's names can't box us in if we don't let them. Our true identity comes from what God says about us and who we belong to.

My Dad always encouraged me to say these uplifting words in the mirror every night: "I am smart, I am sweet, I am funny, I solve problems, I'm a Neuner, and I love Jesus!" I hope that by reading this book, kids and grown-ups alike will find their identity in Jesus and proudly declare to the world, "Are You A Tree?!"

-Dylan Neuner

Dad: Why are you crying?

Daughter: I was playing with the boys
on the playground at school and they said
that I was an ugly, scary, stupid, stinky monster.

Dad: Well...if they say so, then they must be right.

Let's see what else you are.

Dad: Are you a...

Daughter: NOOOO... I AM NOT A TREE DAD!

Dad: Are you a...

Daughter: NOOOO... I AM NOT A CAT DAD!!

Dad: Well then you must be a...

Daughter: DAAAD!!!! I AM NOT A HORSE!!!

Dad: Are you sure? You don't neigh, neigh, neigh, all the time?

Daughter: NO DAD!! I AM NOT A HORSE!!

Dad: I got it! You are a...

Daughter: DAD!!! I AM NOT A HOT DOG.

Dad: Are you sure? You sure look like a hot dog to me.

Daughter: NO!!!!

Dad: Okay, okay! Well, if you aren't a tree, a cat, a horse, or a hot dog, then you aren't an ugly, scary, stupid, stinky monster either!

Dad: Do you want to know what you really are???

Daughter: What Daddy???

Parents: Place a photo of your child inside the frame before reading the story with them.

Heir

Loved

Blessed

Redeemed

Courageous

Free

Chosen

Forgiven

Your Picture Here

Victorious   Beautiful

Teaching Tips for Parents, Grandparents, Aunts, Uncles, Godparents, Guardians, Teachers, and Everyone Who Loves Children!

"You reap what you sow, more than you sow, and later than you sow."
- Charles Stanley

Are You A Tree? is an imaginative, fun, and interactive short story illustrating the value and worth that God, our Heavenly Father, places on us through His only Son, Jesus Christ.

The greatest gift we can give our children is helping them cultivate a deep understanding of the value God places on them and how no one else's words have the power to change that.

The greatest truth of all time is that God loves us! His love is unconditional and boundless. Because of His great love for us, God has provided a way for every one of us to know Him personally through His Son, Jesus. When we place our trust in Jesus, we can enjoy abundant life here on Earth and have the free gift of eternal life with Him in Heaven.

As you read this book with your little ones, here are a few helpful thoughts, questions, and answers you can share:

When we trust our lives to God, we gain everlasting freedom, no matter what happens in our lives.

- Question: How can I get that freedom?

- Answer: By becoming a follower of Jesus and trusting Him, He comes to live in your heart. He is always with you, and nothing can separate you from His love. To receive Jesus in your heart, you can pray the ABC prayer:

  A - Admit that you have done wrong and need God's forgiveness.

  B - Believe that Jesus died on the cross for your sins and came back to life.

  C - Choose to follow Jesus and invite Him into your life.

- Bible Verse: "The Lord is the Spirit, and where the Spirit of the Lord is, there is freedom." (2 Corinthians 3:17 Easy-to-Read Bible Version)

God helps us feel free and happy, even when things are hard.

- Question: How can I feel free and happy when bullies bother me?

- Answer: By trusting in Jesus, you can remember that you are special to God and that He loves you very much. Jesus will help you feel brave and strong.

- Bible Verse: "The Lord is the Spirit, and where the Spirit of the Lord is, there is freedom." (2 Corinthians 3:17, Easy-to-Read Bible Version)

God loves us always and wants us to remember how special we are.

- Question: Does God love me even when bullies bother me?

- Answer: YES! ALWAYS! You are precious and special to God, our Heavenly Father!

- Bible Verse: "This is how God showed his love to us: He sent His only Son into the world to give us life through Him." (1 John 4:9, Easy-to-Read Bible Version)

God made us to be like Him, and He thinks we're amazing!

- Question: What does it mean to be made in God's image?

- Answer: God created us to be like Him and to share His love with others. We are special because God is wonderful.

- Bible Verse: "I praise you because you made me in such a wonderful way. I know how amazing that was!" (Psalms 139:14, Easy-to-Read Bible Version)

God wants us to be kind to ourselves, just like He is kind to us.

- Question: How can I be kind to myself when I keep making mistakes and feel bad about myself?

- Answer: Remember that God loves you, even when you make mistakes. He wants you to learn and grow, but also to be gentle with yourself, just like He is with you.

- Bible Verse: "Bear with each other and forgive one another if any of you has a grievance against someone. Forgive as the Lord forgave you." (Colossians 3:13, Easy-to-Read Bible Version)

Our thoughts and words should be positive and loving, just like God's thoughts and words about us.

• Question: What should I do when I think or say mean things about myself?

• Answer: Stop and remember that God loves you and made you special. Replace those mean thoughts with kind words that God would say about you.

• Bible Verse: "Finally, my friends, keep your minds on whatever is true, pure, right, holy, friendly, and proper. Don't ever stop thinking about what is truly worthwhile and worthy of praise." (Philippians 4:8, Easy-to-Read Bible Version)

God wants us to trust Him and not be afraid of what others think.

• Question: How can I stop worrying about what other people think of me and focus on what God thinks of me?

• Answer: Remember that God loves you and has a special plan for your life. Focus on His love and pleasing Him, not other people.

• Bible Verse: "So don't worry, because I am with you. Don't be afraid because I am your God. I will make you strong and will help you; I will support you with my right hand that saves you." (Isaiah 41:10, Easy-to-Read Bible Version)

Be a good example for others and lead by your actions.

• Question: How can I help stop bullying?

• Answer: Treat others with respect and love. Show yourself kindness to show others what it means to be kind.

• Bible Verse: "Don't let anyone look down on you because you are young. Show other believers how to live by your words, by your actions, by your love, by your faith, and by your pure life." (1 Timothy 4:12 Easy-to-Read Bible Version)

God wants us to be brave and strong no matter what.

• Question: How can I be strong and brave when bullies bother my friends?

• Answer: If you see someone being bullied, you can help by showing kindness to the person being picked on. Be their friend and let them know they're not alone. Tell a grown-up, like a teacher or a parent, about what's happening so they can help too. You can also ask God to give you the right words and actions to help make the situation better. Standing up for others and being kind is a great way to show God's love to everyone.

• Bible Verse: "Be strong and brave. Don't be afraid of those people because the Lord your God is with you. He will not fail you or leave you." (Deuteronomy 31:6, Easy-to-Read Bible Version)

Remember, God wants us to forgive others, just like He forgives us.

• Question: How can I forgive bullies who have hurt me?

• Answer: It can be hard, but with God's help, we can remember that everyone makes mistakes, and we can ask Jesus to help us forgive them. Remember, that by choosing to forgive them and being kind, even if they don't apologize, you are not being weak and are actually being strong. You are representing Jesus and possibly through the Holy Spirit encouraging them to change their behavior.

• Bible Verse: "Be kind and loving to each other. Forgive each other the same as God forgave you through Christ." (Ephesians 4:32, Easy-to-Read Bible Version)

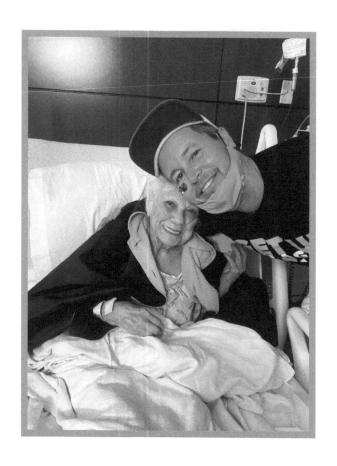

"Now all glory to God, who is able, through his mighty power
at work within us, to accomplish infinitely
more than we might ask or think."
Ephesians 3:20

ACKNOWLEDGEMENTS

To my Lord, Jesus Christ - Thank You for Your grace. Thank You for Your mercy. Thank You for Your healing and Your new creation in me. I pray that you are glorified in this book's creation. I pray for healing for anyone who touches this book and to be brought to a deeper walk with You.

To my wife Corey - You are beautiful. You are my best friend. "There are many virtuous and capable women in the world, but you surpass them all!" Thank you for being a Proverbs 31 woman. Everyone who knows you is blessed for it.

To my children Dylan, Everett, and Chase - For helping keep my soil from going fallow. You help keep me active, alive, and creative and remind me daily that the best days are still ahead of us.

To Kary Oberbrunner, Travis White, and the entire Igniting Souls team and community - Thank you for being the "Who's" that knows the "How" that helps me unlock potential and live into my purpose with this written word.

To my Dad - Thank you for always living courageously. No matter how life crushed you, you always have the courage to get back up and play the game again.

To my Mother - Thank you for living as an example of generosity.

To my Grandma and Grandpa Tilson - Preach the Gospel at all times, and when necessary...use words. Thank you for living this!

To Dan Sullivan and Babs Smith - For providing selfless clarity to others, living as an example of "how the best always get better", and creating the best community in the world to support growth-minded entrepreneurs! It is truly the best playground I have ever experienced!!

To Cathy Davis, Shannon Waller, Stephanie Radia-Bramwell, Sandra Thompson, and the entire Strategic Coach team - All I have to say is... WOW!

To Dean and Joy Dickschat - For being one of the best living examples I know of people who live their faith. Thank you for believing in us and taking a true "leap of faith" with our family. It is a pleasure to own your old toilets and I look forward to cleaning your new ones one day in heaven!

To my many other mentors, inner circles, business partners, teams (special shout out to my Superpowers assistant - Celeena Caccavone for keeping me organized), advisors, friends, clients, and BarnHill Vineyards guests that contribute daily to the richness of my life; there are not enough pages or words to express my love and appreciation for each of you. Thank you! I am a "Spiritual Billionaire" thanks to each of you!

PS. IF I forgot you on this list and your feelings are hurt, then you know I am sorry, and you also know me well enough to know I have a GOLDFISH memory!

LOVE YOU! Neuner

ABOUT THE AUTHOR

A lifetime entrepreneur and learner, Steven Neuner stands out as a leader of compassion and innovation in every industry in which he operates. He started his first business in his twenties out of the guest bedroom of his home with no money, capabilities, or connections. With a ton of hustle, grit, and the love and support of his wife, Corey, who is also his business partner and best friend, Steven has helped build, scale, and operate multiple multi-million-dollar companies. It's in the success of others that Steven's joy blossoms.

His mission is to help others find freedom, clarity, and joy. His passion is empowering others to make wise business and life decisions that allow them to realize their full potential. "Money is just a byproduct. Helping people is the real reward," Steven says. Steven became a Christ-follower later in life and believes that to live into God's purpose, one must live a perfectly imperfect life and balance growth while living comfortably uncomfortable. Steven and Corey enjoy family adventures with their three children, huge extended family, and closest friends.

For more about Steven and to download free coloring pages from this book, please visit StevenJNeuner.com.

Enjoy Steven's Other Book

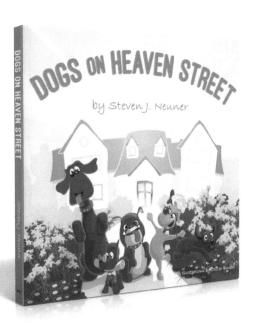

AVAILABLE WHEREVER BOOKS ARE SOLD.

REACH NEW LEVELS OF FREEDOM & GROWTH

Steven Neuner Will Help You Get A Leg Up!

START THE CONVERSATION TODAY

STEVENJNEUNER.COM

THIS BOOK IS PROTECTED INTELLECTUAL PROPERTY

The author of this book values Intellectual Property. The book you just read is protected by Easy IP™, a proprietary process, which integrates blockchain technology giving Intellectual Property "Global Protection." By creating a "Time-Stamped" smart contract that can never be tampered with or changed, we establish "First Use" that tracks back to the author.

Easy IP™ functions much like a Pre-Patent™ since it provides an immutable "First Use" of the Intellectual Property. This is achieved through our proprietary process of leveraging blockchain technology and smart contracts. As a result, proving "First Use" is simple through a global and verifiable smart contract. By protecting intellectual property with blockchain technology and smart contracts, we establish a "First to File" event.

Powered By Easy IP™

LEARN MORE AT EASYIP.TODAY

Printed in the USA
CPSIA information can be obtained
at www.ICGtesting.com
LVHW070002271023
761976LV00018B/393